IMPROVE YOUR LATERAL THINKING

Puzzles to Challenge Your Mind

Paul Sloane & Des MacHale

Illustrated by Myron Miller

Sterling Publishing Co., Inc.   New York

Dedication

This book is dedicated to Woody Allen, Clarence Birdseye, Richard Branson, Edward de Bono, George Boole, Filippo Brunelleschi, Nicolaus Copernicus, Thomas Edison, Albert Einstein, Dick Fosbury, Galilei Galileo, Guglielmo Marconi, Groucho Marx, Sir Thomas More, Sir Isaac Newton, Tom Peters, Leonardo da Vinci, Oscar Wilde, Steven Wright, Orville and Wilbur Wright, and lateral thinkers everywhere.

Edited by Claire Bazinet

Library of Congress Cataloging-in-Publication Data

Sloane, Paul, 1950-
    Improve your lateral thinking : puzzles to challenge your mind / Paul Sloane and Des MacHale; illustrated by Myron Miller.
        p.   cm.
    Includes index.
    ISBN 0-8069-1374-6
    1. Puzzles. I. MacHale, Des. II. Title.
GV1493.S5936   1995
793—dc20   94-46775
                                                                      CIP

10 9 8 7 6

Published by Sterling Publishing Company, Inc.
387 Park Avenue South, New York, N.Y. 10016
© 1995 by Paul Sloane & Des MacHale
Distributed in Canada by Sterling Publishing
c/o Canadian Manda Group, One Atlantic Avenue, Suite 105
Toronto, Ontario, Canada M6K 3E7
Distributed in Great Britain and Europe by Cassell PLC
Wellington House, 125 Strand, London WC2R 0BB, England
Distributed in Australia by Capricorn Link (Australia) Pty Ltd.
P.O. Box 6651, Baulkham Hills, Business Centre, NSW 2153, Australia

Sterling ISBN 0-8069-1374-6

CONTENTS

INTRODUCTION

When the Wright brothers set out to build a flying machine, many intelligent people assured them that their project was a fool's errand. Everybody knew that a machine that was heavier than air could not fly. When Marconi tried to transmit a radio signal from England to Canada, the experts scoffed at the idea of sending radio waves around the curved surface of the Earth. But Marconi succeeded. When Copernicus and then Galileo proposed that the Sun, not the Earth, was the center of the known universe, they were condemned as dangerous heretics. Yet each of these people changed the world by defying conventional thinking and by coming up with a radically new and better solution to an existing problem.

This is the core of lateral thinking—solving problems by the use of creative new approaches. The skills of lateral thinking can be honed by attempting to unravel and piece together what happened in unfamiliar situations, such as the puzzles in this book. This can be great fun and very challenging. Coming up with the answers involves asking the right questions, to ascertain what is really going on in the situation, and then figuring out the answer—not just any possible answer, but the answer given.

Each puzzle has been rated, ranging from 2 (easy) to 4 (very difficult). The rating can be used to score how good you are at solving lateral thinking puzzles. Do the puzzles with a friend and take turns as puzzle setter and solver. The solver can ask questions about the puzzle. The puzzle setter should answer the question with either "yes," "no," or "irrelevant." If the solver solves the puzzle within twenty minutes, then he or she scores the puzzle rating: 2, 3, or 4. If the solver gets stuck, then the puzzle setter can give the solver a clue from the clues section, but each clue costs a point. (Only one clue is provided for easy puzzles.)

So, if you need two clues to help solve a puzzle with a 4 rating, you score two points. If you can score 15 points or more from a sequence of ten puzzles, you are doing well. You will see your scores improve as you progress at asking questions and thinking of lateral solutions.

The puzzles are designed to be fun. As you do them, your skills in checking assumptions, questioning, deduction, using your imagination, and putting the pieces together should all improve. You can apply these same techniques to aid you in problem-solving in everyday life. Who knows? You could conceive a brilliant idea, make a breakthrough, and confound the doubters just like the Wright brothers did!

THE PUZZLES

Easy Puzzles

Recovery *2 points*

A truck driver called in to his office to report that his truck had broken down. A tow truck was sent out to tow back the disabled truck. When they arrived, the truck that had broken down was towing the tow truck. Why?

Clue: 47/Answer: 71.

Man Overboard
2 points

A man holidaying abroad was alone on his yacht when he fell off into deep water. He was a non-swimmer and was not wearing anything to help keep him afloat. He was rescued half an hour later. Why didn't he drown?

Clue: 47/Answer: 72.

High Blood Pressure
2 points

During a medical examination, Gerald's blood pressure is found to be three times that of a normal healthy person. Yet neither Gerald nor his doctor is particularly worried about this. Why?

Clue: 47/Answer: 74.

The Great Wall
2 points

An American, who had never been to any country other than the United States, was standing one day on solid ground when he saw the Great Wall of China with his own eyes. How come?

Clue: 47/Answer: 76.

Poor Delivery
2 points

A Denver company ordered some goods from a European supplier. The American firm was very precise in stating the dates on which it wanted the deliveries to occur. However, the European company, which generally had a high reputation for dependability, missed every delivery date by at least one month. Some shipments were very early and others were very late. Why?

Clue: 47/Answer: 78.

The Pilot's Son   *2 points*

A man and his son were travelling on a scheduled flight across the Atlantic. The man asked the flight attendant if his son could have a look inside the cockpit. The boy was allowed to do this and the pilot gladly explained about the plane and its controls. After the boy left, the pilot turned to the co-pilot and said to him, "That was my son." How could that be?

Clue: 47/Answer: 80.

Hole in One   *2 points*

A golfer had dreamed all her life of hitting her tee shot straight into the hole. However, one day she did this and was not at all pleased. Why not?

Clue: 48/Answer: 82.

Circular Tour   *2 points*

It has often been observed that individuals lost in a desert will set off with the intention of walking in a straight line but will eventually return to their starting point. Why is this?

Clue: 48/Answer: 72.

A Riddle   *2 points*

An old riddle goes like this:

A man without eyes, saw plums on a tree.
He did not take plums and he did not leave plums. How could this be?

Clue: 48/Answer: 84.

9

A Door Too Large

2 points

A man bought a door to fit in a door frame. The door was too large, so he cut off a piece. He found it was too small. So he cut off another piece. This time the door fitted perfectly. How come? (He cut pieces only off the door, he did not cut the frame.)

Clue: 48/Answer: 86.

Radio Broadcast

2 points

One summer a Polish radio station, in an attempt to render a service to listeners, broadcast a noise which was proven to deter mosquitoes while not bothering humans. The station received a barrage of complaints from listeners. Why?

Clue: 48/Answer: 88.

Hide and Seek
                                    2 points

The children had been playing Hide and Seek for some time when Jackie said, "I can't play anymore. It is obvious that anyone could find me now." "It depends who is doing the seeking," said Joan. "Most of us would find you easily, but for John it would be just as hard to find you as anyone else who was hiding." She was right. What was going on?

Clue: 48/Answer: 90.

Dance Ban
                                    2 points

A bar in Rio has a regular dance competition every Thursday night. It banned one man from entering because he kept winning. He was not a professional dancer or schooled in dancing. Why did he keep winning?

Clue: 48/Answer: 92.

The Missing Money
                                    2 points

A man went to a cash-dispensing machine outside a New York bank and withdrew $200, which he carefully put into the back pocket of his trousers. He spent $30 that day. The next day, when he reached into the back pocket of his trousers, he found only $5. Nobody had robbed him. What had happened?

Clue: 48/Answer: 71.

500 Times
                                    2 points

Florence has 500 times as many as Washington. Of what?

Clue: 48/Answer: 72.

The Drive

2 points

A man and woman in a car drove down the drive from their house to the road. The man was behind the wheel. When they reached the road they got out and changed places. The woman turned the car around, then they swapped places again and the man drove back down the drive to the house. They did this several times. Why?

Clue: 49/Answer: 74.

Bouncing Baby

2 points

How could a baby fall out of a twenty-story building and live?

Clue: 49/Answer: 76.

The Tower

2 *points*

A man went to the top of a 180-foot-high cylindrical tower. He leapt off, but was uninjured. Why?

Clue: 49/Answer: 78.

The Slow-Car Race

2 *points*

A special endurance test involved two drivers and their cars. They were told to drive 100 miles out into the desert, rest for no more than one hour, and then drive back. The catch was that the *last* car back would be the winner.

The two drove out very slowly. During the rest period, one of the drivers began to doze. The other driver immediately drove back as fast as he could. Why did he do this?

Clue: 49/Answer: 80.

Homecoming

2 *points*

An executive who was based in New York was posted to Hong Kong on assignment. When he was due to return, he faxed his manager the following request: "Is it OK for me to transport back to New York, at the company's expense, my personal items, household effects, and junk?" He was given approval and did so.

A furious argument ensued. The company refused to pay the transportation charge and, in the end, the executive had to sue the company. He won, but that is not the issue. The question is: What was the cause of the argument?

Clue: 49/Answer: 82.

Bypass

2 points

The people of a small French town were very annoyed by the traffic, especially the heavy trucks, that travelled the one main road running through the town. To eliminate the problem, they built a modern bypass road that was much wider than the road through the town. However, they soon found that they got at least as many trucks going through the town as before. Why?

Clue: 49/Answer: 74.

People Puzzles

The Postman

2 points

A postman had to deliver a letter to a house that was surrounded by a five-foot wall. The house could be approached only by the main path. Unfortunately, a ferocious dog was tied by a long lead to a tree nearby, so that the path was well within the dog's range. If the postman walked up the path, he was sure to be attacked by the dog. How did he outmaneuver the dog and deliver the letter?

Clue: 50/Answer: 84.

The Boss

2 points

One day a boss said to his employees, "I can fight and beat any man who works here." A new employee, a seven-foot-tall ex-prizefighter, stood up to take on the boss. What did the boss do?

Clue: 50/Answer: 76.

14

The Stockbroker   *2 points*

Why did a stockbroker continue to send out to many people forecasts of stock price movements that he knew would be wrong?

Clue: 50/Answer: 88.

The Runner   *2 points*

When a runner reached the end of a long, gruelling marathon, officials were amazed to see him continue to run. Why did he do this?

Clue: 50/Answer: 90.

The Ventriloquist

2 *points*

It was only when he died that the secret of a great ventriloquist was discovered. What was it?

Clue: 50/Answer: 92.

The Golfer

3 *points*

Jones was playing in a golf match that he very much wanted to win. He was on the green and using his putter. He carefully lined up his putt, aimed at the hole, and then deliberately putted the ball right over and beyond the hole. Why did he do this?

Clue: 50/Answer: 71.

The Professors

3 *points*

Two professors of mathematics glared at each other as they examined the same elementary equation. It had been written by a ten-year-old child. "This equation is correct," said one. "No, it is absolutely wrong," said the other. How could two experts disagree so completely about a simple equation?

Clue: 50/Answer: 72.

The Quatorzième

3 *points*

In Paris, a man with a job known as a quatorzième sits in his place of work in the evening. Sometimes he is called on to do something, but most evenings he is not. What does he do?

Clue: 51/Answer: 74.

The Cartoonist
3 *points*

Why does the United States Air Force employ the services of a top-class cartoonist?

Clue: 51/Answer: 78.

The Swimmer
3 *points*

In 1967, Sylvia Ester, an East German Olympic swimmer, swam the 100-metre freestyle in a time of 57.9 seconds, a new world record. But this was never recognized or acknowledged. Why not?

Clue: 51/Answer: 76.

The Climber
3 *points*

A climber bought an expensive new pair of climbing boots. On his first outing with them he found that they were too tight, so he changed into some old boots he had brought. He did not want to carry the new boots all the way up the mountain and back, but he feared that if he left them behind they would be found and kept by another climber. What did he do?

Clue: 51/Answer: 80.

The Salesman
3 *points*

A door-to-door salesman visited a house in order to demonstrate an excellent new model of vacuum cleaner. As part of the demonstration, he emptied a small bag of soot on a carpet. To his embarrassment the vacuum cleaner would not pick up the soot. Why not?

Clue: 51/Answer: 82.

The Secretary

A secretary went on vacation. She inadvertently took with her something from the office. Her boss sent her a message asking her to return it immediately. This she did. Yet, when she returned from vacation, she was dismissed. Why?

Clue: 51/Answer: 84.

The Millionaire

4 points

A man working late at the office left some sandwiches on his desk. As a result of this, he later became a multi-millionaire. How?

Clue: 52/Answer: 78.

The Engineer   *4 points*

An engineer was studying a dam when he was suddenly killed. How?

Clue: 52/Answer: 86.

The Farmer   *4 points*

A greedy and miserly farmer worked hard and tended his crops very carefully. Suddenly, he dashed out one day and dug up a field that had a crop of half-grown hay. It was a little wet, but there was nothing wrong with the crop. He subsequently had to resow the field, and the whole episode cost him much time and money. Why did he do it?

Clue: 52/Answer: 88.

The Investigator   *4 points*

A private investigator followed a man. He waited until the man parked his car and went off. The investigator then let the air out of one of the tires on the man's car. Waiting at a distance, he watched as the man returned, examined the flat tire, and then walked off. The investigator then went home, pleased with his day's work. What had he been hired to do?

Clue: 52/Answer: 90.

WALLY Test I

Now is the time to test your wits with a quick-fire WALLY test. Get out a pencil and paper and write down the an-

swers to the following questions. You have two minutes to complete the test. Answers cannot be changed once written down and you must not look at any of the solutions until you have completed the test. Be warned that WALLY tests sometimes contain trick questions of a kind designed to catch you out!

1. On which side of a cup is it best to have the handle?

2. Where do the biggest potatoes grow?

3. Who was the first man mentioned in the Bible?

4. Where did Noah strike the last nail in the ark?

5. What living thing has only one foot?

6. What did Paul Revere say at the end of his epic ride?

7. Would you rather a tiger attack you or a lion?

8. What is it that Adam, the first man, never had and never saw yet he left to his children?

9. What kind of dog, found in every country, has legs but never runs?

10. Where are all men equally good-looking?

See WALLY Test solutions on page 76.

Crime Puzzles

Robbery 2 points

A gang of criminals was loading a van with television sets that they were stealing from a warehouse when they suddenly heard the siren of an approaching police car. They could not avoid or outpace the police car. How did they escape?

Clue: 53/Answer: 92.

Great Detection 2 points

A masked robber passed a note to a bank teller. It said,

"I've got a gun. Hand over all the money in your till." The teller did so and the robber made good his escape. Within twenty-four hours, the police had arrested him. What mistake had he made?

Clue: 53/Answer: 86.

Headline News   2 *points*
· ·

A jury found John Jones guilty of murder, and the judge passed the death penalty on him. The judge then returned to his chambers, sat down for a cup of coffee, and picked up a copy of the afternoon paper. The headline read, "John Jones Guilty—Sentenced to Death." The judge was baffled that the paper could have printed the story in so short a time. How could they?

Clue: 53/Answer: 72.

The Bad Driver   2 *points*
· ·

James was a notoriously bad driver. He always drove much faster than the speed limit, through red traffic lights, and up one-way streets the wrong way. He was known to the police as the worst and most dangerous driver in town. Yet, for twenty years, he did not have any kind of motoring accident, was not arrested or cautioned by the police, and kept a clean license. How come?

Clue: 53/Answer: 77.

Point-Blank Shot   3 *points*
· ·

A man walked up to a naked woman, pointed a gun at her heart, and shot her. She survived. How?

Clue: 53/Answer: 78.

The Trial
3 points

A man was on trial for the murder of another man, despite the fact that the body had not been found. During the trial there was a sensational announcement that the man who had been murdered was, in fact, alive and in the next five seconds was about to enter the courtroom. The murdered man, however, did not arrive, and the prosecutor then claimed he could prove the defendant guilty. How?

Clue: 53/Answer: 80.

The Forgery
2 points

A forger spent years studying the U.S. $100 bill until he produced what he felt was a perfect forgery. However, he was arrested the first time he tried to pass one. Why?

Clue: 54/Answer: 82.

Poisoned
3 points

An old man was poisoned. The police found that he had eaten and drunk nothing on the day of his death. How had the poison been administered?

Clue: 54/Answer: 86.

The Unhappy Patient
3 points

A man suffering from pains was examined by a doctor who correctly diagnosed the condition. The doctor did nothing. The pain went away. The man was unhappy. Why?

Clue: 54/Answer: 85.

The Unsuccessful Robbery   *3 points*

A gang of armed robbers burst into a large bank. They demanded all the money from the tills. The bank manager pointed out that there was none. They then insisted that he open the safe. He did so but there was no money inside. Just then the police arrived and arrested the gang. What was going on?

Clue: 55/Answer: 71.

The Burglary   *4 points*

A couple went on holiday, leaving their house empty but well secured. They had left their keys with a very careful and honest neighbor. When they returned, they found that they had been robbed of many valuables including jewelry, video equipment, etc. There was no sign of any break-in. How had it happened?

Clue: 55/Answer: 88.

The Golden Vase   *4 points*

A very valuable golden vase was in the middle of a large room in a museum. It was surrounded by an electronic field that formed a complete sphere around the vase. If anything pierced the electronic field, the alarm bells would ring and guards appear in seconds. An enterprising thief worked out a way to break into the museum, but he knew that, if he set off the alarm, the guards would arrive before he could escape with the vase. How did he steal the vase and escape without being caught?

Clue: 55/Answer: 90.

Murder

4 points

An elderly woman is found dead in her bed. She has been murdered. In her bedroom is a fine collection of plates. The police established that she was in good health, seemed perfectly fine when she went shopping the day before, and that no one else had recently visited or entered the house. How did she die?

Clue: 55/Answer: 92.

A Shooting

4 points

At a party two men, Rob and Bill, became engaged in a violent quarrel. Rob pulled a gun and, in plain view of many witnesses, shot Bill dead. The police were called. They questioned Rob and the witnesses. They decided that it was a case of murder, yet they pressed no charge against Rob. Why not?

Clue: 55/Answer: 71.

Another Shooting
4 *points*

A police officer shot a woman dead. Someone else was charged with her murder and found guilty. How come?

Clue: 56/Answer: 72.

Speeding
4 *points*

A man who was driving well in excess of the speed limit was chased by a police car for several miles. Then the man saw another police car in front of him on the road so he pulled over. The officers from both cars came over to him. They had both clearly seen him speeding, yet neither arrested him nor gave him a ticket. They simply gave him a warning and let him go. Why?

Clue: 56/Answer: 74.

Difficult Puzzles

Export Drive
3 *points*

During the 1930s, how did some Japanese businessmen overcome American mistrust of goods made in Japan?

Clue: 56/Answer: 77.

Bombs Away
3 *points*

A bomber plane, which was in perfect working order, was over its target. The tea that the pilot had been drinking sat in its cup at his elbow. The plane released its bombs, but they did not fall from the plane. Why not?

Clue: 56/Answer: 85.

Space Shuttle
3 *points*

Why is it that a plane is allowed to take off and fly in a thunderstorm, but the space shuttle is not?

Clue: 57/Answer: 80.

Suspense
3 *points*

A man travelling by train awoke to find his rail car suspended twenty feet in the air. Why?

Clue: 57/Answer: 82.

The Woman in the Ditch
3 *points*

A beautiful woman walked across a field several times. She deliberately walked in a six-inch ditch. Why?

Clue: 57/Answer: 90.

Grease
3 *points*

A man covered the head of a stranger in grease. Why?

Clue: 57/Answer: 89.

Small Furniture

3 points

A factory specializes in producing furniture that is twenty percent smaller than normal furniture. The furniture is not designed for or sold especially to smaller-sized people. Why do they make it?

Clue: 57/Answer: 86.

Cash in Hand

3 points

Smith had owed Jones a thousand dollars and, although Jones asked for the sum many times, Smith never paid it back. Then one day Smith offered to repay Jones the thousand dollars in cash, but Jones refused to accept it. Why?

Clue: 57/Answer: 91.

The Nosy Student   *3 points*

Judy, a young woman studying at college, was unfortunate to have a roommate who was rude, lazy, selfish, and inquisitive. Judy was annoyed because, while she was at lectures, her roommate would look through Judy's desk and read Judy's personal mail. How did Judy overcome this problem?

Clue: 58/Answer: 78.

Poor Equipment   *3 points*

A man took an expensive piece of equipment with him on a journey. When he reached his destination he found that the equipment, though in perfect working order, was of practically no use. Why not?

Clue: 58/Answer: 86.

Stand at the Back   *3 points*

During a flight from Brazil to London, the pilot told all the passengers to get out of their seats and to stand at the back of the plane. Why did he do this?

Clue: 58/Answer: 71.

The Book   *3 points*

A man walked into a bookshop and bought a book even though he could not understand a word of the language in which the entire book was written. Why did he buy it?

Clue: 58/Answer: 73.

Anywhere in the World   *3 points*

A pilot was due to fly his plane from one place to another when a man asked if he could be given a lift. The pilot said, "Yes, for a small fee that is possible. I can drop you off on my way." "But you don't know where I am going," replied the man. "Surely that makes a big difference." "Not at all," said the pilot. How could this be so?

Clue: 58/Answer: 75.

Police Visit   *3 points*

Before you can buy a car in Tokyo, the police must first come and visit you. Why?

Clue: 58/Answer: 77.

Large and Small

3 points

Why, on the same day, were several groups of strong, fit, large people taking instructions from puny, small people?

Clue: 59/Answer: 79.

Pentagon Panic

3 points

One day during the cold war, a young officer rushed into his superior's office in the United States Department of Defense in Washington, D.C. "We have discovered," he said, "that if both we and the Russians launch our missiles at exactly the same time, their missiles would hit the United States before our missiles hit Russia." "Are our missiles slower?" asked his superior. "No, they have exactly the same power, weight, and speed." "Is the distance they fly shorter?" "No, both distances flown are exactly the same." "Well, what is the reason?" Can you tell?

Clue: 59/Answer: 80.

Page 78

3 points

Every week a woman went into the local library. If she saw a book that looked interesting, she immediately turned to page 78 before deciding whether she should borrow the book or not. Why?

Clue: 59/Answer: 91.

The Statue

3 points

A huge and very heavy statue had to be lifted onto a large pedestal base in the middle of a town square. The bottom of the statue was completely flat and there was no way of lifting it except by putting ropes around and under it. How did they manage to get the ropes out from under the statue once it was lifted onto the base?

Clue: 59/Answer: 75.

The Service

A man regularly used and paid for a particular service that was provided by large organization. The organization announced that, as a special promotion, it would offer all customers the service for one week at one-tenth of the normal price. The man refused this offer and continued to pay the normal price during the special promotion week. Why did he do this?

Clue: 59/Answer: 85.

Historical Puzzles

Jam Doughnut   *2 points*

Why did a famous statesman and world leader stand up in front of a large group of people and say, very seriously, "I am a jam doughnut"?

Clue: 60/Answer: 82.

Without Drought   *2 points*

How did the American Civil War lead to a reduction in droughts in various parts of the world?

Clue: 60/Answer: 77.

Cross the Gorge   *3 points*

It was decided to build a suspension bridge over a deep and wide gorge. The river at the bottom of the gorge was too violent for any boat to cross. How did the engineers get the heavy cables from one side of the gorge to the other?

Clue: 60/Answer: 73.

The End of the War   *2 points*

How do we know that the war between Lydia and Media in Asia Minor ended on precisely May 28, 585 B.C., in our dating system?

Clue: 61/Answer: 87.

The Stiff Gate

3 points

Several people were invited to dinner in a private house. They found that it was quite difficult to open the front gate as it was very stiff. At dinner, one of the guests commented on this and the host smiled. He then explained why he had made the gate hard to open. What was the explanation?

Clue: 61/Answer: 79.

The Twelve

3 points

From the beginning of time and up to the time of this writing, twelve and only twelve people have achieved this feat. What is it?

Clue: 61/Answer: 89.

Across the River

3 points

In the early days of exploration in America, a group of explorers came to a deep, wide river. There was no bridge, and they had no boats or material to make boats. They could not swim. How did they get across?

Clue: 61/Answer: 89.

Brunelleschi's Challenge

3 points

Filippo Brunelleschi is one of the great figures of the Italian Renaissance; he was a sculptor, goldsmith, and architect. His greatest masterpiece is the dome of the cathedral in Florence, which he completed in 1417. He had to win the commission for the dome against stiff competition. The story is told that he won by issuing a challenge to his competitors to stand an egg upright on a flat table without using any other materials. No one else could do it. How did Brunelleschi do it?

Clue: 61/Answer: 85.

Houdini's Challenge 3 *points*
· ·

The great conjurer and escapologist Harry Houdini was an expert with locks and safes. He was once challenged by a safe manufacturer to open a locked safe. Before accepting the challenge, Houdini examined the safe carefully and saw that it was of a new design that he would almost certainly find impossible to unlock. Nevertheless, he accepted the challenge, and won it. How?

Clue: 61/Answer: 87.

The Building 3 *points*
· ·

A man was very relieved one day to reach a building and go inside. It was a place he normally disliked. There was no one there to meet him, and there was nothing for him to do there. Why was he so pleased?

Clue: 62/Answer: 91.

The Forgery 4 *points*
· ·

A historical researcher was presented with a document purported to be an authentic mid-eighteenth-century bill signed by the King of England. How did he know at once that it was a forgery?

Clue: 62/Answer: 81.

The Impostor
4 points

A woman once came forward and claimed to be Anastasia, heiress to the Russian throne. How did the authorities quickly discover that she was an impostor?

Clue: 62/Answer: 73.

Homing Spaniards
4 points

During the early days of their conquests of Central and South America, Spanish soldiers often had to travel long distances through strange, uncharted country. Sometimes they travelled at night. They developed an excellent method of ensuring that they could always find their way back to their base. How?

Clue: 62/Answer: 75.

Motionless
4 points

A young man combed his hair and then sat in a chair for twenty minutes without moving a muscle. Why did he do this?

Clue: 63/Answer: 92.

The Courtier
4 points

King Alfonso XIII of Spain (1886-1931) apparently employed a man at court with just one specific function in relation to music. What was that function?

Clue: 63/Answer: 87.

WALLY Test II

Now for another WALLY test. Get a pencil and paper and give your best answers to the following questions. You have two minutes!

1. How can you drop a raw egg onto a concrete floor without cracking it?

2. If it took eight men ten hours to build a wall, how long would it take four men to build it?

3. Which would you prefer to have, an old ten-dollar bill or a new one?

4. Approximately how many birthdays does the average Japanese woman have?

5. If you had three apples and four oranges in one hand and four apples and three oranges in the other hand, what would you have?

6. How can you lift an elephant with one hand?

7. What do you always get hanging from apple trees?

8. How can a man go eight days without sleep?

9. Why are so many famous artists Dutch?

10. Divide twenty by a half and add ten. What is the answer?

See WALLY Test solutions on page 83.

. . . .

Gruesome Puzzles

Ageless   *2 points*
. . . .
A young couple were separated shortly after they met and they did not come face to face again for fifty years. By that time he had become an old man, but she had not aged at all. In fact, she looked exactly as he had seen her fifty years before. Why?

Clue: 63/Answer: 79.

The Accident

2 points

A careless driver caused an accident. Fortunately, both he and the driver of the other car were wearing seat belts and were uninjured. However, a passenger in the other car (who was not wearing a seat belt) was very badly mangled in the accident and lost both his legs as a result. When the case came to court the careless driver escaped with a small fine. Why was the judge so lenient?

Clue: 63/Answer: 93.

The Rock

2 points

A man, going about his business, brushed against a rock. Within minutes he was dead. Why?

Clue: 63/Answer: 81.

The Breeze

2 points

A man was standing up on a bright sunny day, happy to feel the breeze in his face. He knew that if the wind dropped he would die. Why?

Clue: 63/Answer: 81.

The Cruel King

3 points

Two men were asked by their king to carry out a certain task. They did this entirely to his satisfaction and went to him seeking their just reward. However, the king decreed instead that they both be severely punished. Why did he do this?

Clue: 64/Answer: 91.

The Nonchalant Wife
3 points

A woman came home one evening and switched on the light in her living room. She was horrified to see the remains of her husband lying on the floor. He had committed suicide. Ignoring the situation, the woman had a cup of coffee and went calmly about her housework, and did not phone for medical assistance or the police. Why not?

Clue: 64/Answer: 85.

Two Men
3 points

A man died a nasty death and another man many miles away was at last happy even though they had never met and no grudges were borne. What was going on?

Clue: 64/Answer: 87.

Too Polite
3 points

Japanese office workers strive to be very polite. One was killed because he was too polite. How?

Clue: 64/Answer: 79.

The Deadly Climb
4 points

A group of healthy men walked up a mountain. One of them died. If the man who died had climbed the mountain on any other day, he would have lived. What happened?

Clue: 64/Answer: 81.

Dead Man, Dead Dog   *4 points*

A man and his dog were found dead in the middle of a field. The man was wearing wading boots. No one else was around. How had they died?

Clue: 65/Answer: 73.

Axe Attack   *4 points*

A woman knocked on a stranger's door and asked to use the bathroom. She came out and killed the man with an axe. Why?

Clue: 65/Answer: 77.

A Mysterious Death   *4 points*

A healthy man went out for a walk one evening and was later found dead. The police examined the body carefully but were mystified as to the cause of death. No one else was involved. A postmortem revealed that the man had been killed by a freak accident that left virtually no trace. What was it?

Clue: 65/Answer: 87.

The Man Who Shot Himself   *4 points*

A man who was alone in a room very carefully and deliberately pulled out a gun and shot himself. Some time later, another man was charged with his murder and found guilty. What happened?

Clue: 65/Answer: 73.

Fiendish Puzzles

Light Saving   *4 points*

In the subway of a major American city, the stealing of light bulbs was a common occurrence and a major problem. The sockets for the light bulbs were within easy reach and could not be moved. How did the city authorities solve this problem and practically eliminate the theft of light bulbs?

Clue: 66/Answer: 81.

Matchless   *4 points*

A particular person born in January 1978 has a unique distinction. What is it?

Clue: 66/Answer: 75.

The Less-Costly Capital   *4 points*

One of the world's capital cities spends much less (both as a proportion of its budget and in absolute terms) than other capital cities on a social service which is generally considered vital. Why is this?

Clue: 67/Answer: 83.

An Odd Number   *4 points*

What is peculiar about the number 8549176320?

Clue: 67/Answer: 85.

Bus Stop I

4 points

A man is standing at a bus stop carrying an ordinary kitchen chair in his hands. Why?

Clue: 67/Answer: 87.

Bus Stop II

4 points

A woman travels by bus to a certain building every day. There are two bus stops on her side of the street. One is 100 yards before the building and the other is 200 yards beyond the building. She always gets off at the bus stop 200 yards past the building and walks back. Why?

Clue: 67/Answer: 91.

Stop/Go
4 points

A group of responsible people, not pranksters, drive around a city in their car. When they stop for a traffic light, they do not go, even if the light has turned green, until a car behind them toots its horn. Why do they do this?

Clue: 68/Answer: 93.

Vanishing Point
4 points

A man paid a great deal of money to travel to an exotic location, but when he returned he found that he had never really been there at all. Why? Where was it?

Clue: 68/Answer: 75.

Western Sunrise
4 points

As we all know, the sun rises every day in the east and sets in the west. One day, a man saw the sun rise in the west. How?

Clue: 68/Answer: 77.

The Signal
4 points

John stood in an enclosed room watched by three men. The room had no windows or openings, but solid walls, floor, ceiling, and door. There was no telephone or electrical device of any kind. The three men (who all had good eyesight and hearing) watched John carefully in silence. They observed no change in condition, sound, or movement. Yet, while they were watching, John signalled to his partner, James, in a nearby room and passed a message to him. How?

Clue: 68/Answer: 79.

45

One Inch Shorter

4 points

A man went to work one day and by the end of his day's work he was one inch shorter. Why?

Clue: 69/Answer: 79.

Teenage Party

4 points

While his parents were away, a teenage boy and his friends drank some of the parents' gin. This was of course strictly forbidden. They then poured water into the gin bottle to return the level to where it had originally been, and put the bottle back exactly where they had found it. However, when the couple came home, the father took one look at the bottle of gin and turned angrily to his son to denounce him for illicit drinking. How had he known?

Clue: 69/Answer: 81.

THE CLUES

Easy Puzzles

Recovery

There was nothing wrong with the tow truck. The truck that had broken down had a serious fault which was remedied by the way they drove back.

Man Overboard

The previous day he had bought some beautiful postcards of Jerusalem.

High Blood Pressure

Gerald's blood pressure is normal for Gerald.

The Great Wall

He had travelled a long way to see a sight that very few people have seen.

Poor Delivery

The misunderstanding was based on a problem with written communication. Each company followed exactly the same written instructions but interpreted them differently.

The Pilot's Son

No stepfathers, grandparents, or in-law relationships are involved. The passenger was the father of the pilot's son.

Hole in One

She hit one shot and her ball finished in the hole, but this did not count as a hole in one.

Circular Tour

What we think of as equal are often not equal.

A Riddle

He had sight and he took fruit.

A Door Too Large

He had to take two cuts from the door to make it fit. Both cuts were from the length of the door. The width and thickness remained the same.

Radio Broadcast

The high-pitched noise achieved its intended purpose of driving off mosquitoes while being inaudible to humans.

Hide and Seek

Jackie's condition had changed such that she was now much easier to find. John had a disability which gave him no advantage in finding Jackie.

Dance Ban

The other contestants thought he used a low trick, but it was really just a natural advantage in this kind of dance.

The Missing Money

Nobody else was involved. At the end of the first day there was $170 in his trouser pocket. The next day he had $5 in his trouser pocket.

500 Times

This is a physical difference and, for the purposes of the

puzzle, it may be assumed that Florence and Washington are about the same size and age.

The Drive

They had never done this before, but once they started they followed this same procedure for several weeks: swapping places where the drive met the road. Then they never did it again.

Bouncing Baby

The baby was a normal human baby and it fell onto the hard sidewalk, but lived.

The Tower

There were no safety nets, ladders, or scaffolding. If he had jumped from the other side of the building, he would have been killed.

The Slow-Car Race

The desert and the full fuel tanks are not important here. What is important is that the last car back wins the race for its owner. The driver raced back in order to win the race.

Homecoming

The cost of transporting the goods home was very high. The company claimed that the executive had misled them over what he wanted to bring back, but he showed the court that he had been accurate in his description.

Bypass

In this true incident, trucks continued to pour through the town, although cars used the new road.

People Puzzles

The Postman

He did not use anything to distract the dog except himself.

The Boss

The boss kept his word, but did not beat the man or back down.

The Stockbroker

He sent out many predictions, but he was not a good predictor.

The Runner

He knew that he had reached the end of the race, but he kept on running because he had a good reason to run.

The Ventriloquist

The ventriloquist could do much better tricks with one dummy than with his other dummies.

The Golfer

He was playing regular golf in which one plays from tee to green and tries to do so in the fewest strokes.

His previous shot had been a very poor one.

The Professors

The two professors each saw a simple written equation. But, for a very basic reason, they saw it differently. This made it right for one, but wrong for the other.

As they argued about this they looked straight at each other.

The Quatorzième

His work consists of eating a meal in a restaurant.

He always eats in a large group, but generally with people he has never met before and has nothing particularly in common with.

The Cartoonist

The cartoonist is employed to draw cartoons, but not for entertainment or amusement.

The cartoons are used in pilot training.

The Swimmer

There was nothing amiss with the pool, the water, or the ambient conditions. The problem of recognizing the time concerned Sylvia Ester.

She was a well-known swimmer who had won many other events in recognized times. But there was something different about her swim this day.

The Climber

He hid the boots, but in a way that, even if they were found, it was unlikely they would be taken.

They were a fine pair of climbing boots.

The Salesman

There was nothing wrong with the vacuum cleaner. It was in perfect working order.

He had had a long drive to reach the house.

The Secretary

She had taken a key. She posted it back immediately.

She was dismissed because she posted it back.

The Millionaire

The man is very famous.

The sandwiches that were left out were eaten by a visitor whose actions inspired the man.

He could draw very well.

The Engineer

He stood on the river bank watching the dam, which was in excellent condition.

He was killed accidentally by one of the dam's constructors.

Although he had heard about this kind of dam before, he had never seen one and he marvelled at its construction. No mechanical aids or formal training had been used.

The Farmer

He had had no intention of ploughing up the field until he had awoken that morning.

He ruined the crops in the forlorn hope of a much larger harvest.

He was superstitious.

The Investigator

The private investigator had a camera.

The man was under investigation for fraud.

The investigator was gathering evidence for an insurance company.

Crime Puzzles

Robbery

The gang did not attempt to flee. They thought laterally. The police did not.

Great Detection

The police examined all clues left at the scene of the crime and quickly knew where they could find the robber.

Headline News

The editor of the newspaper had not known what the jury's verdict would be, but he ensured that his newspaper was available, with the correct headline and story, as soon as the trial finished.

The Bad Driver

Although he always drove badly, he committed no offense in this twenty-year period.

Point-Blank Shot

The gun was a real handgun in full working order, firing real bullets that would normally kill someone.

She was the kind of person who would make every effort to improve her career.

The Trial

The prosecutor had arranged for the announcement of the missing man's "return," knowing full well that it would not happen.

The accused man knew that the missing man could not return.

The Forgery

He was nearly arrested for a driving offense that very morning.

Poisoned

He had followed his normal daily routine unaware that someone had planned to poison him. He had met no one else on the day of his murder.

He had inadvertently put the poison into his mouth.

The Unhappy Patient

The doctor took an X-ray.

The patient was warned that "anything found may be used in evidence against you."

The Unsuccessful Robbery

Their timing was very poor.

The bank had had plenty of money at the start of the day.

The Burglary

The neighbor had allowed access in, but had watched every action they made like a hawk.

Something had apparently been delivered in error.

Valuable pictures, which were mounted high on the wall, had not been stolen.

The Golden Vase

He hid in a small broom closet near the vase.

He came from Australia.

He convinced the guards that the alarm was faulty.

Murder

The police discovered that she had been poisoned. They checked all the food and drink in the house and could find no trace of poison.

She had bought many fine plates, but rarely went to shops or markets.

The day before her death she had been to the grocery store and the post office.

A Shooting

Rob was not a police officer, nor was he acting in self-defense. Bill was not a criminal. His murder was in no way justified.

Rob had had no intention of killing Bill. The police were satisfied that someone other than Rob was the murderer.

Their professions are important.

Another Shooting

The policeman did not shoot the woman deliberately.

The man who was found guilty of the woman's murder had placed her in danger.

The police were trying to save the woman.

Speeding

The police officers would have liked to have booked the man, but they could not. Both officers had given out several other speeding tickets that day, and they were eager to do it again.

The man was not a doctor or a diplomat. He had no good excuse or exemption.

The answer relates to jurisdiction. Although the man had clearly committed an offense, and although a police officer with jurisdiction was present to give out speeding tickets, the man could not be given a ticket.

Difficult Puzzles

Export Drive

They relocated their premises within Japan.

They made a true but misleading statement on their goods.

Bombs Away

The bomber was in the air at a height of 20,000 feet and over its target. It was flying right-way-up (unlike a similar, classic puzzle where the pilot could *not* be having tea). The mechanism was in working order, but the bombs, when released, did not fall from the plane.

The bombs fell.

Space Shuttle

This has nothing to do with the materials that the space shuttle is made of, nor with the radio communications.

The direction of the shuttle's flight and the nature of its exhaust are relevant.

Suspense

This was a regular occurrence on this particular railway. It allows an essential change to take place.

Although the rail car being lifted so high in the air does shock new passengers, the reason for this action is not difficult for them to gauge.

The Woman in the Ditch

She was an actress.

She wanted to appear shorter than she really was.

Grease

The man had a benevolent purpose in mind and the stranger was pleased to have the grease rubbed all over his head.

The man was in uniform, the stranger was not.

Small Furniture

They make the furniture for a special kind of house.

The furniture is seen by many but used by very few.

Cash in Hand

Smith offered to pay Jones the thousand dollars at a time when it would have been disadvantageous for Jones to accept it.

Whichever of them had the money would lose it shortly.

The Nosy Student

Judy hid her letters in the shared room, but in a rather good hiding place.

The roommate was a very poor student.

Poor Equipment

The piece of equipment was a watch.

The man took it somewhere on Earth where there is no official time.

Stand at the Back

There was an emergency and passengers were in danger.

It had nothing to do with how the plane was flying or weight distribution.

The Book

He did not buy it for the pictures, illustrations, style, or appearance of the book. Nor did he have any intention of reading it or learning the language it was written in.

He was thrilled to get the book and eager to show it to his friends.

Anywhere in the World

The pilot was due to fly from one place to another such that, wherever the passenger wanted to go, it would be on the pilot's route, and dropping the passenger off would hardly make any difference to the pilot's total flight time.

Think of the Earth as a sphere.

Police Visit

The purpose of the police visit has nothing to do with your driving skill or the condition of the car.

The population of Tokyo is over sixteen million people.

Large and Small

All the groups of people were engaged in the same activity.

The large, fit people were chosen for their strength. The small people were chosen for their light weight and their judgment.

Pentagon Panic

This has nothing to do with technology, rocket design, wind, or weather.

The same missile would get from Moscow to New York faster than it would get from New York to Moscow. If missiles were launched by both countries at the same time, the Russian missile would strike first. The reverse would be true for the same missiles going from Alaska to Vladivostock in eastern Russia. Then, the American missile would strike first.

Page 78

She was not looking for a particular book, but for books in general that were interesting and new.

Her husband read the books.

The Statue

No ramps, slides, or levers were used. The statue was not tilted or dropped.

The statue was lowered using ropes. The ropes were removed. The statue then settled very slowly onto the base.

The Service

The man paid more for the same service as everyone else in the expectation of future gain.

The man was a collector.

Historical Puzzles

Jam Doughnut

He was in a foreign city.

Without Drought

A technique was learned for increasing rainfall.

Cross the Gorge

This happened over a hundred years ago, before planes or rockets could be used. The engineers could cross the gorge only by travelling miles downstream.

Just as the world's entire population is descended from Adam and Eve, so a small beginning can lead to a great outcome.

The End of the War

An unusual event marked the end of the war. It is an event that nowadays we can date with great precision.

The Stiff Gate

The host was a famous inventor and engineer.

The guests, in pushing open the gate, were performing a useful job for the host.

The Twelve

The twelve people who have achieved this feat were all men. They were not especially rich or influential or exceptionally talented, but they were intensively trained.

The twelve people who have done this all did it within a ten-year period in the 1960s and 1970s.

Across the River

They got across without getting wet.

They did not use any additional materials, but crossed the deep, wide river easily.

Brunelleschi's Challenge

The table was flat and horizontal. The egg was a regular hen's egg, not cooked or treated in any way. He made the egg stand on the table without any other materials or items.

The other contestants made an assumption about what they were allowed to do. This assumption stopped them from seeing the solution that Brunelleschi used.

Houdini's Challenge

He did not use any special equipment or explosive. He knew that he could not unlock the safe using a conventional approach, so he used a lateral approach.

Although the safe manufacturer and onlookers witnessed the feat, they could not see how Houdini managed to unlock the safe door.

The Building

He was a thief who had fled.

This took place many years ago.

The Forgery

There was nothing wrong with the general appearance of the document, the paper it was on, or the signature of the king.

The date on the document indicated to the expert that it was a forgery.

The date was a day in 1752, which would appear normal to many people. The expert knew that the document could not have been printed or signed on that particular date.

The Impostor

The woman answered all their questions faultlessly and agreed to undergo any tests they requested.

The real Anastasia had a medical condition that would not have been immediately apparent even to a doctor. The woman underwent no medical tests.

Her agreement to take a test was seen as evidence that she was an impostor.

Homing Spaniards

They did not mark the path in any particular way, nor did they memorize the route.

They rode out and rode back. No other people, birds, or animals served as guides.

Some of them rode stallions, but certainly not all of them did.

Motionless

He was a perfectly healthy person and free to move, but he sat still voluntarily.

There was another person in the room. He was performing a service for the first man, but they never touched.

This took place during the nineteenth century.

The Courtier

The courtier did not have any particular musical skill, but he had a good memory.

The king had a particular affliction.

The courtier was called into use on certain state occasions.

Gruesome Puzzles

Ageless

They had been involved in an accident. He had aged, but she was perfectly preserved.

The Accident

The driver's car was white. The other car was black.

The Rock

He was uninjured, but the rock damaged his suit.

The Breeze

He was standing still but moving slowly.

The Cruel King

The king did not punish the men for any wrongdoing on their part, but rather for his own selfish reasons.

Their punishment was execution. It meant that they could never present a threat to the king.

The king was miserly, selfish, cruel, and very rich.

The Nonchalant Wife

Even though she found her husband's remains on the floor, the woman had no reason to call any authorities.

The woman was horrified to see her husband's remains on the floor, but not at all surprised that he was dead.

Two Men

The death of one man resulted in a benefit to the other.

The man who was happy was not responsible for the other man's death, but he knew exactly when it would happen.

Too Polite

The polite man did not say anything. He simply made a very polite action at an unfortunate time.

He was in a large office, going from one department to another.

The Deadly Climb

Climbing conditions were perfect as the men all walked up the high mountain. The dead man's companions were un-harmed, but he died a painful death.

The man was an enthusiastic, all-round sportsman. He climbed the mountain in the afternoon.

It was what the man did in the morning which lead to his death on the mountain.

Dead Man, Dead Dog

The man had been fishing illegally in a lake.

In desperation the man had run away from the lake, but to no avail.

The dog was a retriever.

Axe Attack

When the woman entered the house she had no idea who the man was and had no intention of doing him any harm.

It was while the woman was in the bathroom that she realized who the man was and decided to kill him.

The woman had seen the axe before.

A Mysterious Death

The man died an accidental but highly unusual death.

There was a tiny hole in his head.

Thousands fly through the air, but very few reach the ground.

The Man Who Shot Himself

The man shot himself with his own gun and with the immediate intention of killing himself. He had no history of suicidal tendencies, insanity, phobias, or psychological disorders.

The two men met shortly before the man shot himself. No words were spoken when they met, but because of the murderer's actions the man shot himself.

Both men were gangsters.

Fiendish Puzzles

Light Saving

The only thing that was changed was the design of the light bulb and its socket.

The bulbs could still be removed by hand by the city engineers and maintenance staff.

The bulbs could be reached by hand by anyone, but the vandals found that, try as they might to unscrew the bulbs, they could not remove them.

Matchless

The individual was the first person ever to have been born under certain circumstances.

From a medical or biological point of view, there was nothing unusual about the person's birth.

The location of the person's birth was singular.

The Less-Costly Capital

The city spends less in this service area than other cities spend because it has less need to spend.

The service on which this capital city spends less is fire-fighting.

The city is not particularly cold or damp, yet its geography makes fires less likely.

An Odd Number

You need no mathematical skills to solve this problem.

Note that each digit is used once.

The sequence of the digits is significant.

Bus Stop I

The man would have liked to have sat on the chair while he waited for the bus, but he could not.

The man was unhappy, and the chair was the cause of his unhappiness.

When he got on the bus, the man had difficulty paying his fare.

Bus Stop II

The woman does not meet anybody or pass anything of interest or benefit to her by going to the farther bus stop. She does not like exercise.

When the woman comes home, she walks to the nearer bus stop in order to catch the bus.

The woman finds it easier to walk 200 yards from the far bus stop, rather than 100 yards from the near bus stop.

Stop/Go

The individuals are not color-blind or disabled in any way.

Their purpose and approach is serious and includes the use of a stopwatch, pencil, and paper.

From time to time the people change one aspect of the vehicle they are driving.

Western Sunrise

No mirrors or reflections are involved. The man saw the celestial sun rise in front of him in the west.

He was on the planet Earth, not in a space rocket, or in space, or at the North or South Pole.

Looking west, the man first saw the sun set, then a little later he saw it slowly rise again.

Vanishing Point

The place the man wanted to go to is well known, but very few people go there.

The man was taken to the famous place and saw what he expected. He later discovered that it had not really been the famous place, but no one had deceived him.

The place is marked, but it is not on land.

The Signal

John did not have any special extrasensory or psychic powers.

James received the signal, but not by sight or touch or feel.

John often went out with James for a walk together.

One Inch Shorter

The man was fit and healthy, as was necessary for his physically demanding job.

Nothing was cut off the man—he became an inch shorter as a result of an incident at work.

He was subjected to enormous forces.

Teenage Party

The boy and the house gave no clue to the fact that the boy had been drinking.

The place where the gin was kept is relevant.

The father did not like a lot of ice in his gin and tonic.

THE ANSWERS

Recovery

The truck had broken down because its brakes had completely failed. The truck driver drove back towing the recovery vehicle. When he needed to slow, he signalled with his hand and the recovery truck driver applied his brakes, thereby slowing both vehicles.

The Missing Money

The man had on a different pair of trousers in which he just happened to leave five dollars.

The Golfer

Jones was on the wrong green. Two different holes had greens that were fairly close. The two holes lay in a straight line. Jones hit his putt hard in the direction of the other green.

The Unsuccessful Robbery

The gang had arrived at the bank shortly after another gang had robbed the bank.

A Shooting

Rob and Bill were actors playing out a scene for a television crime series. Unbeknown to Rob, someone with a grudge against Bill had substituted real bullets for the blanks that should have been in Rob's gun.

Stand at the Back

A passenger sitting near the front had smuggled a poisonous snake onto the plane and it had escaped.

Man Overboard

He fell into the Dead Sea, which lies between Israel and Jordan. The water of the Dead Sea is so salty and dense that anyone in it floats very easily.

Circular Tour

Most people take one stride that is ever so slightly longer than their other stride. Over a period, this results in their walking in a huge circle. Incidentally, most athletes have a right stride longer than their left stride, relating to the fact that they always run clockwise around athletic tracks.

500 Times

Hairs on the head. Florence is a brunette, and Washington is a bald man.

The Professors

The equation was $9 \times 9 = 81$ but they were looking at it from different sides of the table. So to one professor it was correct, but to the other it read $18 = 6 \times 6$, and so was wrong.

Headline News

The editor knew that this trial was the big story of the day, so he had two versions of the newspaper printed—one with the story that Jones was found guilty, and one with Jones found innocent. He then simply distributed the correct version.

Another Shooting

In this true case, a robber had taken a woman as a hostage after his robbery. When the police tried to free her there was a shoot-out. The hostage was found to have been shot by a police bullet. The court decided that the robber had been guilty of her murder.

The Book

The man was the author of the book. On a visit to Tokyo, he recognized the cover design and was delighted to see that it had been translated into Japanese. He was more than happy to buy the book to show to his friends.

Cross the Gorge

Very light fibres were sent across the gorge attached to a kite. These fibres were then used to pull strings across, which were used to pull ropes across, and so on until heavy cables were stretched across the gorge.

The Impostor

The authorities asked the woman to take a blood test, and she agreed. The real Anastasia was a hemophiliac, who would never have consented to a blood test.

Dead Man, Dead Dog

The field was next to a lake. The man had been poaching fish by dynamiting them. He threw a stick of dynamite into the lake. Unfortunately, the dog chased the stick, retrieved it, and carried it to the man, who had run away across the field—but to no avail.

The Man Who Shot Himself

This is based on an actual case. The men were members of rival gangs. When they met, one pulled a knife and stabbed the other in the stomach, leaving him to die slowly and in agony. The dying man shot himself to curtail the pain. The prosecution proved that the man would have died soon after from his stab wounds. The court found the man who had carried out the knife attack guilty of murder.

High Blood Pressure

Gerald is a giraffe. The average blood pressure of a giraffe is three times that of a human being. This higher pressure is needed to pump the blood up that long neck!

The Drive

The man was just learning to drive. He did not yet have a license, which would have allowed him to drive on the road, but he could drive on their private drive. The woman, his mother, turned the car around at the road so that he could continue to practise by driving back along their long drive.

Bypass

When the bypass was built, a bridge was built over it so that townspeople living nearby but on the other side of the bypass could still easily reach the town market. Unfortunately, the bridge over the bypass was not high enough to allow the passage of trucks underneath, so their drivers had to continue using the road through the town.

The Quatorzième

He works in a major restaurant and, if called upon, it is his job to join a party of thirteen people in order to bring the number up to fourteen. Thirteen is considered a very unlucky number when dining in Paris.

Speeding

The man sped out of one country and stopped just over the border in another. The first policeman, who had chased him, had no jurisdiction in the second country. The second policeman had jurisdiction but could not arrest or prosecute the man for the speeding offense because it had taken place in another country.

Anywhere in the World

The pilot was due to fly from one point to another lying exactly opposite on the surface of the Earth. If we consider the Earth to be a sphere, then there are an infinite number of routes from a point A to a point B diametrically opposite to it. The pilot could set off in any direction and still have the same flight time. It follows that it would be possible to plan a straight course from A to B which would pass over the place where the other man wanted to go.

The Statue

Blocks of ice were placed on the pedestal so that the ropes on the bottom of the statue fitted between them. The ropes were then withdrawn. As the ice melted, the statue was lowered until it lay firmly on the base.

Homing Spaniards

Whenever possible, the Spanish explorers took with them a mare who had recently given birth to a foal. They left the foal at their base. The mare would invariably lead them back.

Matchless

He was the first child born in Antarctica, and therefore the only person who is known to be the "first born on a continent."

Vanishing Point

The place was the North Pole. The point is marked on the ice pack over the Arctic Sea. The ice pack drifts, and from time to time the point has to be adjusted. When he returned, the man read that the point marking the North Pole was being relocated.

Bouncing Baby

The baby fell out of a first-floor window.

The Boss

He fired the new employee on the spot!

The Swimmer

In this actual incident, the officials refused to recognize Sylvia Ester's achievement because she swam in the nude.

· ·

WALLY Test I

· ·

Here are the WALLY test answers:

1. The outside.

2. In the ground.

3. Chap 1.

4. On the head.

5. A leg.

6. Whoa!

7. You would rather the tiger attack the lion.

8. Parents.

9. A dead dog.

10. In the dark.

Rate your score on the following scale:

Number Correct	Rating
8 to 10	Wally Whiz
6 to 7	Smart Alec
3 to 5	Wally
0 to 2	Ultra-Wally

· ·

The Bad Driver

James never drove his car during this period.

Export Drive

Many Japanese exporters relocated their factories to a little Japanese town called Usa. They could honestly stamp on their products MADE IN USA.

Police Visit

The Japanese police first verify that you have a garage or parking space and then give you a permit to buy the car. Parking space is so scarce in Tokyo that, if you have no parking space, you are not allowed to own a car.

Without Drought

During the American Civil War it was noticed that the continued firing of cannons caused an increase in rainfall. From this it was learned that firing guns into clouds could cause them to release their water vapor in the form of rain.

Axe Attack

This incident occurred during the French Revolution. The woman had seen her father beheaded at a public execution by a masked executioner wielding a large axe. The man kept the axe in his bathroom (he had to keep it somewhere!). When she saw the axe, the woman knew that the man must have been the executioner who had killed her father.

Western Sunrise

He was the pilot of the Concorde. It took off shortly after sunset and flew west. It, therefore, caught up with the sun and the pilot saw the sun rise in front of him—in the west.

Poor Delivery

The U.S. company stated its required delivery dates in its usual date format, i.e., month/day/year. The European company read the dates as European date format, i.e., day/month/year. So, if the American company asked for a delivery on the 5th day of July 1995, shown as 7/5/95, the European company would deliver the 7/5/95 shipment on the 7th of May!

The Tower

The tower was the Leaning Tower of Pisa. The man jumped off on the upper side and landed safely on the floor below.

The Cartoonist

He draws cartoons in which small objects are concealed. The drawings are used to test the ability of trainee pilots to detect targets in camouflaged backgrounds.

The Millionaire

The man was Walt Disney. A mouse came to nibble the sandwiches and it behaved so comically that Walt put out some food for him every night. The mouse inspired the idea of Mickey Mouse, hence the Disney empire.

Point-Blank Shot

This true story concerns a striptease dancer who was shot by a jilted boyfriend. Although naked, she was saved by a silicon breast implant that stopped the bullet.

The Nosy Student

Judy hid her letters in her roommate's textbooks, as she knew that was the one place that the roommate would never look.

Large and Small

The strong, fit, large people were oarsmen taking instructions from their coxes in preparation for a rowing regatta.

The Stiff Gate

The host was Thomas Edison, the famous inventor. He explained that everyone who opened his stiff gate pumped ten gallons of water into his rooftop tank!

Ageless

The couple had been rock climbing together and they fell. He was rescued, but her body was trapped in a glacier. He was present when her body was finally recovered fifty years later.

Too Polite

The Japanese office worker was in an elevator at work. The doors opened and he saw an important senior executive. He bowed low and his head was caught in the closing elevator doors.

One Inch Shorter

He was an Air Force jet pilot who had had to eject after a mid-air collision. The ejector seat threw him out with an enormous acceleration of over one hundred Gs. This acceleration compressed the vertebrae in his back making him an inch shorter. After medical treatment and rest, he recovered to his normal height.

The Signal

John stood with a dog whistle in his mouth. He gave three low whistles to his pet dog, James, to signal him to come and sit. The frequency of a dog whistle is too high for the human ear to hear but is audible to a dog.

The Pilot's Son

The pilot was the boy's mother.

The Slow-Car Race

The driver who raced back had jumped into his opponent's car, thus ensuring that *his* car would arrive back last and he would win.

The Climber

He hid one boot behind a rock and then hid the other a short distance farther on. He reasoned that, whereas one boot may be found, it was unlikely that the same person would find both boots, and since one boot would be of little or no value it would not be taken.

The Trial

While those in the courtroom watched the door and waited for the missing man to appear, the accused man was being videotaped. When the video was later played for the jury, they could see that the defendant did not even glance towards the door—he knew that the missing man was dead and could not return.

Space Shuttle

The exhaust plume of the space shuttle effectively grounds the space shuttle for a considerable part of its initial flight. Therefore, the shuttle could be struck by lightning. A plane is not grounded, so does not conduct lightning.

Pentagon Panic

The missiles are thrown up out of the Earth's atmosphere and then plunge back to Earth. The Earth's rotation, therefore, affects their flight times. Since the Earth rotates from west to east, it follows that a missile will have a shorter flight time from Moscow to New York than vice versa.

The Forgery

When the calendar was adjusted in England in 1752, eleven days were skipped. The date on this document was one of the eleven days that never existed!

The Breeze

The man was windsurfing from Cuba to the United States in a desperate attempt to reach freedom.

The Rock

The man was a deep-sea diver. The sharp rock punctured his suit.

The Deadly Climb

The man who died had been scuba diving in the sea that morning. Ascending to the high altitude so soon gave him an attack of the "bends," where nitrogen dissolved in the bloodstream decompresses and is released as bubbles. It was this that killed him.

Light Saving

The sockets were adapted so that bulbs with a left-hand screw were used. Unlike most other bulbs in sockets, they had to be twisted clockwise to be released. When would-be thieves tried to unscrew the bulbs, they were unwittingly tightening them.

Teenage Party

The father kept his bottle of gin in the freezer, where gin remains liquid even to very low temperatures. The watered-down gin, however, had frozen into a solid block within the bottle.

Hole in One

She got a hole in one—but on the wrong green! Driving off the first tee, she holed out on the adjacent, 18th, green.

Homecoming

In this true story, the executive had had shipped back to New York a thirty-foot sailing junk (Chinese boat) that he had bought while in Hong Kong.

The Salesman

The house was remote. When the salesman went to plug in the vacuum cleaner, he found that there was no electricity supply in the house.

The Forgery

He was red-green color-blind. The note was colored red. (He had problems with traffic lights as well as paper!)

Suspense

The man was travelling on the Chinese railway system where, for historical reasons, at a certain point the gauge of the rails changes from narrow to wide. Rail cars are lifted bodily twenty feet in the air before being deposited on a frame with wheels of wider track.

Jam Doughnut

President John F. Kennedy, on his visit to Berlin, tried to express solidarity with the people of the city by saying in German, "Ich bin ein Berliner." Unfortunately, he had been badly advised, since the phrase "ein berliner" in common German use did not mean an inhabitant of Berlin but a jam doughnut.

The Twelve

Only twelve men have walked on the surface of the moon.

WALLY Test II

Here are the WALLY test answers:

1. Concrete floors are very hard to crack!

2. No time at all—it is already built.

3. An old ten-dollar bill is worth ten times as much as a new one-dollar bill.

4. Just one. All the others are anniversaries.

5. Very large hands.

6. It is not a problem, since you will never find an elephant with one hand.

7. Tired.

8. He sleeps at night.

9. They were born in Holland.

10. Fifty. Dividing by a half is the same as multiplying by two.

Now rate your score on the following scale:

Number Right	Rating
8 to 10	Wally Whiz
6 to 7	Smart Alec
3 to 5	Wally
0 to 2	Ultra-Wally

The Less-Costly Capital

The capital city in question is La Paz, Bolivia. It is the world's highest capital, lying between 10,700 and 13,200 feet (3300 and 4100 metres) above sea level. At this altitude there is less oxygen and fires do not light easily. La Paz has very little need of a fire service, and so saves money.

A Riddle

The answer lies in the use of plurals. He did not have eyes, he had one eye. He saw two plums on a tree. He took one and left one, so he did not take "plums" or leave "plums."

The Postman

The postman walked around the outside of the wall. The dog followed him, gradually winding its lead around the tree. The effective length of the lead was eventually reduced so much that the dog could no longer reach the path, so the postman delivered the mail.

The Secretary

She had taken the only key to the office mailbox. She posted it back, so it wound up in the locked mailbox!

The Unhappy Patient

The man had stolen some diamond rings and swallowed them just before his arrest. The police doctor X-rayed him. He was charged. Then they simply waited for the loot to be recovered.

Bombs Away

The plane was already in free-fall.

The Service

The man was a stamp collector. The regular postage charge for a letter was around thirty cents but, as a special promotion, the post office declared that all letters posted during a certain week need only carry a three-cent stamp. He continued to use the regular stamps on the letters he sent to relatives, friends, and to himself, during that week, knowing that the stamped envelopes would be rare and become valuable to collectors.

Brunelleschi's Challenge

Brunelleschi brought the egg firmly down onto the table, thereby cracking and slightly flattening one end. The egg then stood on end. All the other contestants had assumed that the egg must remain unbroken, but this was never a condition.

The Nonchalant Wife

The woman's husband had committed suicide three years earlier. The cat had knocked over the urn containing his ashes. After she finished her cup of coffee, she swept his remains back into the urn.

An Odd Number

In the number 8549176320, the digits are arranged in alphabetical order.

The Great Wall

He was an astronaut standing on the moon—from where the Great Wall of China is visible.

A Door Too Large

This one is really a "snip"! The piece he cut off was too small, so he cut another piece off. The "it was too small" refers to the piece he had cut off, not the door.

The Engineer

The engineer was killed when a large tree fell on him. The dam the engineer went to see had been built by beavers, and a particularly industrious one felled the tree.

Great Detection

He had written the note on the back of an envelope that had his name and address on the front!

Poisoned

The poison had been put on his false teeth.

Small Furniture

The furniture is put into show houses on new housing estates. The smaller furniture makes all the rooms look larger.

Poor Equipment

The expensive piece of equipment was a very good watch. The man went to the North Pole, where all the world's time zones meet. Although the minute hand would be correct, the hour hand could be set to any of the time zone hours. There is, in effect, no "correct time" at the North Pole!

The End of the War

It is recorded that the war ended on a day when there was a total eclipse of the sun. Each of the armies took the eclipse as a sign that the gods were angry with them. Astronomers can date the eclipse very accurately.

Houdini's Challenge

He offered to "make the challenge even more difficult" by being locked inside the safe. He had guessed correctly that the safe was far easier to unlock from the inside than from the outside.

The Courtier

King Alfonso XIII of Spain was completely tone deaf. The man's function was to tell the king when the national anthem was being played, so that he could stand up.

Two Men

The man who died was executed in a Malaysian jail for drug smuggling. The other man was in hospital in Hong Kong awaiting a kidney transplant. He had arranged to buy the kidneys of the executed man.

A Mysterious Death

The unfortunate man had been hit by a tiny meteor that had penetrated his brain.

Bus Stop I

While repairing the chair, the man had accidentally stuck his hands to it with superglue. He was waiting for a bus to go to the hospital to have the chair removed from his hands.

Radio Broadcast

The noise that deterred the mosquitoes was a frequency too high for the human ear to hear. It drove away mosquitoes, but also, unfortunately, cats and dogs. Listeners complained that their beloved pets fled when the broadcast sound came on.

The Stockbroker

The stockbroker was trying to launch his own business. He bought a mailing list of 4000 wealthy people and sent half of them a prediction that IBM stock would rise the next week. He sent the other half a prediction that IBM would fall. A week later, he chose the 2000 names to whom he had given the correct forecast, and split them into two. Half received a forecast that Exxon would rise. The other 1000 received a forecast that Exxon would fall. Those who received the forecast that came true were again divided, and so on. After doing this six times, the broker was left with 62 people who had all received from him a sequence of six correct forecasts! They, naturally, thought that the stockbroker was a fantastically accurate predictor of market movements.

The stockbroker then called each of them in turn and asked them to move their entire portfolios to his control. They readily agreed, and he had the large portfolio base he needed.

The Farmer

When the farmer awoke that morning he had seen a rainbow in the sky. It seemed to end in his field. He dug up the field in order to find the pot of gold!

The Burglary

The couple had given their keys to an honest and conscientious neighbor. One day a delivery van had arrived. The van driver told the neighbor that he had a chest of drawers ordered by the couple for delivery. The neighbor unlocked the house and carefully watched the van driver and his mate carry the chest of drawers inside. An hour later, the van driver returned and apologized; he had delivered the chest to the wrong house. The neighbor again watched as the chest was removed. Hidden within this piece of furniture was a dwarf. He had, of course, removed all the small valuables he could found during his stay inside the house.

Across the River

They walked across; the river was frozen.

The Accident

The other car was a hearse, and the passenger was already dead.

Hide and Seek

Jackie had a sudden attack of the hiccups. These were so loud and regular that most of children easily heard her. John, however, was deaf.

The Runner

In this true incident, the man had been let out of prison for the day in order to enter the marathon. After completing the race, he kept on running to avoid returning to prison.

The Investigator

The man had made a claim against his employers for an industrial injury that he claimed had damaged his back so severely that he could no longer bend down. The private investigator had been hired to gain evidence that this was not so. He took photographs of the man bending down to examine his flat tire.

The Golden Vase

The thief hid in a broom closet after closing time at the museum. He opened the closet door and threw a boomerang which broke the electronic field before returning to him. He quickly grabbed the boomerang and retired to the closet. The guards came running but found everything in order. When they went away, the thief repeated the feat. This happened several times. Eventually, the guards decided that the electronic system was malfunctioning and they switched it off. The thief then sneaked out and replaced the vase with a replica.

The Woman in the Ditch

She was the co-star in a movie and was playing opposite Alan Ladd, who, though a fine actor, was rather short. So as not to be seen towering over her co-star, the woman walked in a specially cut channel alongside Alan Ladd.

Cash in Hand

Smith and Jones were travelling on the subway when a gang of muggers came into the car and started to take everyone's money. Smith offered to repay his debt to Jones just before the robbers reached them.

Page 78

The woman was borrowing books for her disabled husband who was confined to the house and a voracious reader. She could not remember which books he had already read, so they had a scheme. Whenever he read a book, or if she brought back a book he did not like, he made a small pencil mark at the bottom of page 78. She could then tell which books to avoid.

The Building

It was in medieval times and the man was on the run from a group of angry traders whom he had robbed. He reached a church and claimed sanctuary within it. His pursuers could not arrest him in the church and, if he waited long enough, he could get away.

The Cruel King

The king had asked the men to design and build the world's strongest strongroom, where he could safely keep his treasures. Once he was fully satisfied with the workings of the strongroom, he had the men executed so that they could tell no one its secrets.

Bus Stop II

The road on which the building stands is on a steep hill. The woman prefers to go past the building and walk down the hill, rather than alight earlier and walk up the hill.

Dance Ban

The dance contest is a limbo dancing competition. The man banned was a dwarf, who had a natural advantage in getting under the low bars.

The Ventriloquist

The great ventriloquist was really only an average ventriloquist with a clever partner. He started his act with a standard routine with one or two different dummies. Then he would reach into a large chest and pull out another "dummy," who was really a dwarf that dressed and acted like a dummy. The rapid and humorous dialogue of the two men fooled the audience into believing they were seeing a virtuoso performance in ventriloquism.

Robbery

They started to unload the television sets and carry them back into the warehouse. When the police arrived, the robbers told the police that they were making a late delivery, and they were believed!

Murder

The elderly woman was poisoned by her greedy nephew, who wanted to inherit her fortune. He sent her what looked like a mailer with a fantastic offer for a collector plate which he knew she would want to have. To order the plate, the offer had to be completed, folded and sealed, and sent back without delay. The nephew had put a slow-acting poison on the seal of the mailer. Once his aunt had licked the seal and posted the mailer, there was nothing to connect him to her murder.

Grease

The man's head had been stuck in a railing. A fireman rubbed grease on the captive's head to help free him.

Motionless

The man was having his portrait taken in the very first days of photography.

Stop/Go

The people are graduate psychology students conducting an experiment to measure the popularity of various foreign nationalities. In Paris, the students placed German, British, Italian, or Spanish number plates and ID stickers (D, GB, I, E) in turn on the cars. They then drove around, stopping at lights, and measured the length of time it took for French motorists to lean on their horns after the lights changed. They were testing a theory—the shorter the time, the more unpopular the nationality shown on the car!

INDEX

Page key: **puzzle,** *clue,* solution

About the Authors

PAUL SLOANE was born in Scotland and grew up near Blackpool in the north of England. He studied engineering at Trinity Hall, Cambridge, and graduated with a first-class honors degree. While at Cambridge he met his wife, who is a teacher. They live in Camberley, England, with their three daughters.

Most of Paul Sloane's career has been in the computer industry and he is currently the European vice-president for a software company. He has always been an avid collector and creator of puzzles. His first book, *Lateral Thinking Puzzlers*, was published by Sterling in 1991. Paul Sloane has given speeches and radio talks on the topic of change management and lateral thinking.

DES MACHALE was born in County Mayo, Ireland, and is Associate Professor of Mathematics at University College in Cork. He was educated at University College, Galway, and the University of Keele in England. He and his wife, Anne, have five children.

The author of over thirty books, mostly of humor but also one on giving up smoking, Des MacHale has many interests including puzzles, geology, writing, broadcasting, films, photography, numismatics, and, of course, mathematics. He is currently working on three more books.

This is the third book co-authored by Paul Sloane and Des MacHale. It follows on the success of *Challenging Lateral Thinking Puzzles* and *Great Lateral Thinking Puzzles*, also published by Sterling.